Sorry, Lady—This Beach Is Private!

Also by James Stevenson:

DO YOURSELF A FAVOR, KID

THE SUMMER HOUSES

Sorry, Lady—
This Beach Is Private!

Cartoons by *STEVENSON*

THE MACMILLAN COMPANY, NEW YORK

Printed in the United States of America

The Macmillan Company, New York
Collier-Macmillan Canada, Ltd., Toronto, Ontario

Library of Congress catalog card number: 63–17514

"By golly, *it is* a maraschino cherry!"

"What's for chow?"

"As far as I'm concerned, gentlemen, this marks the end of the Schwarzwälder String Quartet."

"Generally speaking, I love a parade, but I don't care much for this one."

"Golly! You sure gave my truck a smack, didn't you?"

"They're making a little too much of this bankruptcy business."

"*Do we have any absinthe?*"

"I believe our quest is ended."

"He was a __nice__ Pharaoh."

"In a way, I hate to do it. That's one of the finest examples of twelfth-century fortified Norman."

"Are you sure this is Channel 13?"

"We're Little People, too. We're Summer Little People."

PARENTS' NIGHT

"This is where we keep our blanket for our rest."

"We were thrilled with Freddy's last ashtray."

"No wonder the Hansen child is a discipline problem."

"Which is yours?"

"*Just between us, Miss Swope, what do you think of my boy?*"

"*If you ask me, this college-entrance thing is going to get
a lot worse before it gets any better.*"

"*In our house, all we hear is 'Sandy Phillips this' and 'Sandy Phillips that.'*"

"*If there are no more questions, we'll have our cookies now.*"

"I must say this was the worst-led migration I've ever been on in my life."

"Mr. Lawrence has asked me to make a very special announcement. There will be holidays this month on Washington's Birthday, Lincoln's Birthday, and Mr. Lawrence's Birthday."

"We'll dispense with the horn this morning. You might wake the President."

"What do you say we take one more quick look at that address?"

"This summer, Bert, I smell trouble."

"Top drawer, that chap. Who else would think of waving goodbye?"

"*It's probably some kind of Democratic trick.*"

"Now, because you guys won such a great victory last Saturday, before we look at the movies of the game we're going to run off a couple of Mickey Mouses."

"This model features worn-out equipment, which causes excitingly real hotboxes, delays, and other true-to-life malfunctions."

"Congratulations, Mr. Sullivan. You are now monarch of all you survey in a north-by-northeasterly direction."

"There's something sad and sort of poetic about these places in October."

"Hey, Mac! You see a Polaris come whooshing up a minute ago? Which way did it go?"

"*Just between us, I'm beginning to feel uneasy with Blackwell at the helm.*"

"*He's a great executive, but he's not the easiest guy in the world to work for.*"

"When Louise and I decided to build, we were determined not to put up just another split-level or ranch-type."

"Remember now, only one starfish per person."

SUMMER RENTAL

"Why do you think the plumber snickered when
I said we were in the Calhoun house?"

"Guess what! Bound volumes of 'Motor Age,' 1901–1909."

"I said the Winslows aren't here . . . they went to Europe . . . and rented their house to us . . . the Winslows aren't here . . ."

"Now we know one thing.
If there is one to the garage, it's not among these."

"Pardon me, but isn't there a Gristede's anywhere around here?"

"Kelp."

"On our first day! It wouldn't dare!"

"We might as well put it back.
They say garbage was yesterday."

"A jar of chutney, a marshmallow,
and two ant buttons."

xcuse me, but do you by any chance know where the key
the Palmers' might be if it isn't where it's supposed to be?"

"See? Water."

"Could I have a word with you, sir?"

"We were hoping for one of those airy little
beach houses on stilts, but I'm afraid we started late."

". . . wait till you hear a click. Then turn the
handle to the left as far as it will go . . ."

"I hardly know how to break the news,
we feel so utterly dreadful about it.
That exquisite blue vase . . ."

"He retired last January, but he's been tapering off gradually."

" 'I must go down to the seas again, to the lonely sea and the sky,
and all I ask is a tall ship and a star to steer her by.' John Masefield. Right, Herb?"

"Phone for you, Al."

"Do you suppose, Bancroft, that for the duration of your term as a
director of International Consolidated you could possibly forgo tilting?"

"All right, let's clam up, everybody. Here comes another expedition."

"This the way to the turnpike? We're escaping from a Senior Citizens' Planned Community."

"If the Modern Museum doesn't snap it up, Sam, the Bufferin people certainly will."

"Why is it, Oogluk, that though the years may come and the years may go,
you still never fail to find it amusing when someone slips and falls on the ice?"

"*Just because a fellow happens to agree with me once in a while doesn't make him a yes man in my book.*"

"*That's what it says, all right—'Ostrogoths Go Home.'*"

"*Anderson, my boy, if you truly believe that commercialism should be taken out of Christmas, perhaps you ought to consider whether you really belong in the department-store business.*"

ANTIQUES

"A lady in there told me there's an even <u>better</u> place only about twenty miles up the road!"

"*I don't care what anyone says, Mr. Bartley.*
I don't think you're a robber."

"*I suppose all the really good Early American*
has been snapped up by the White House."

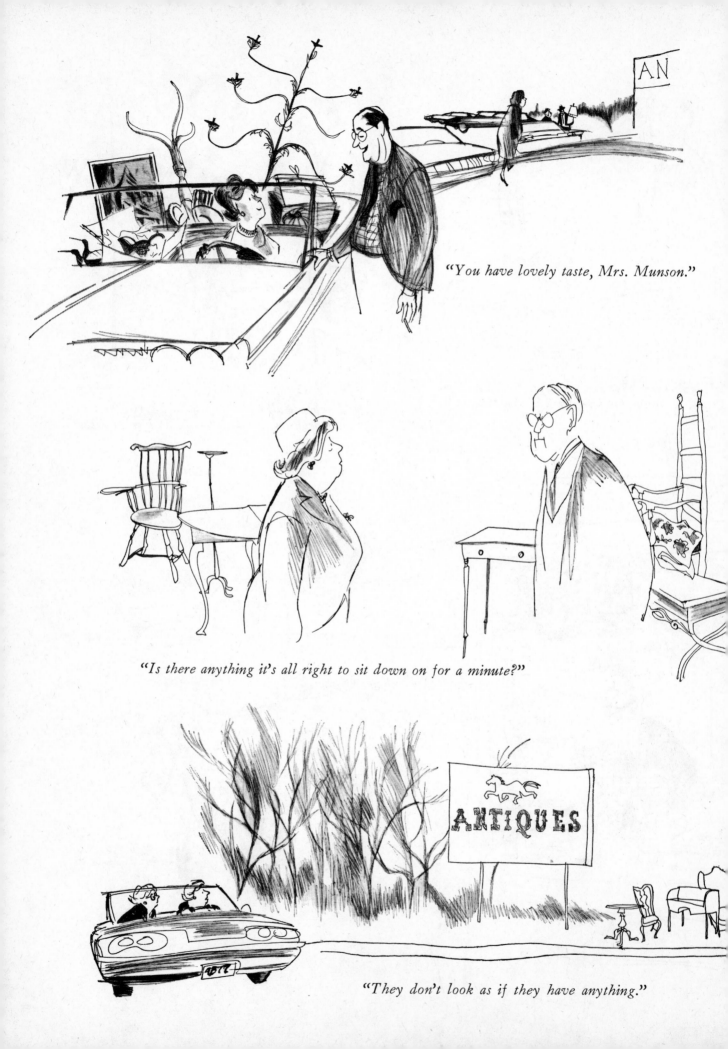

"You have lovely taste, Mrs. Munson."

"Is there anything it's all right to sit down on for a minute?"

"They don't look as if they have anything."

"Have you ever heard of a little place around here that's just _loaded_ with Lowestoft?"

"Harold, do you want to look at a perfectly marvellous Chippendale serpentine-fronted commode?"

"Have I seen everything?"

"Suddenly I'm scared to go home."

"*Once a year, we encourage them to go ahead and get it out of their systems.*"

*"Don't let's panic now—at least until
we see whether he likes peanut butter and jelly."*

"I'm afraid that joke was vulgar without being funny."

"You seem troubled, Brother Timothy. Is anything worrying you? I mean besides the sins of the world, the vanities of mankind, and that sort of thing."

"How many children?"

"*The soup was stone-cold, those goblets were cheap, the goose was raw, the jugglers were awful, the jester was not very funny, the hall was drafty, and as for* her *. . .*"

2   3

"*Eleven.*"

"I've just completed a sort of survey. Every single person here has now told me that he despises cocktail parties."

"Several of us on the board of directors, Baldwin, feel that we are not being consulted on major policy questions."

"*Correct me if I'm wrong, Bernice. This is Jones Beach, this is* 11 A.M., *this is Saturday, this is July 2nd.*"

"That's right. Don't bother to knock. Just barge the hell in."

"Now we owe *them* an orgy."

UP TO THE GAME

"*The Simpsons said they were coming, but I don't see them.*"

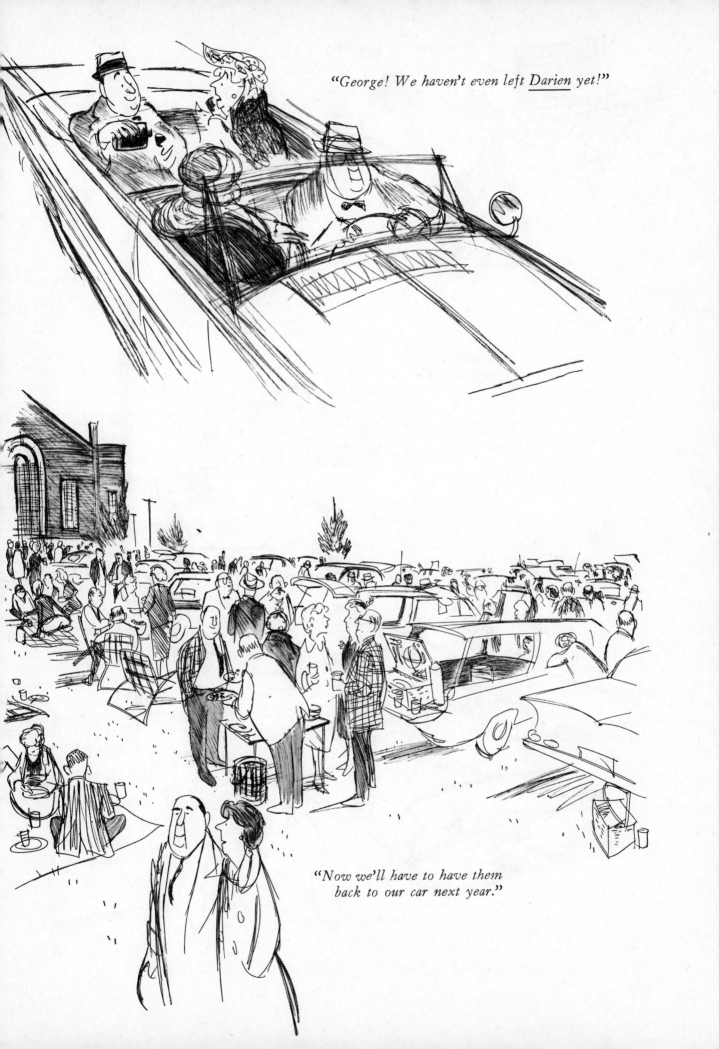

"George! We haven't even left _Darien_ yet!"

"Now we'll have to have them
back to our car next year."

"First and ten _what?_"

"The score is now 13–6, and believe me,
folks, this is one of the most thrilling games in the annals of Ivy League competition."

"Hit 'em hard! Do you
hear me? Hit 'em hard!"

"I want you to remember one thing, Son, and don't
ever forget it. Never pass on first down."

"Quick, Alice, piccalilli or no piccalilli?"

"Excuse me, but we have to be in Far Hills at seve

"You should have seen this Mr. Bartlett go around end carrying three tacklers all the way."

"I'd like to get on that phone for about two minutes."

"*Well, our Physics Department is a hell of a lot better than their Physics Department.*"

"I don't say it had anything to do with the collapse of their civilization. I merely say it dates from that period."

"By this time tomorrow, fellows—if our calculations are correct—Ralphie Sanford here will be in orbit."

"*I can't help thinking how sad we're all going to feel when we have to leave the place next September.*"

"*That certainly is a lousy cornucopia, Demetrius.*"

"Around here, ancient tea ceremony gone way downhill."

"Look. When they said come on over for some singing, was I supposed to ask what kind?"

"If and when, Colonel—can I be in your junta?"

"Say, would you be interested in coming North with us to have a little fun
with the Hempstead, Long Island, Bird Watching Society?"

"How about Nelson Rockefeller as President, David Rockefeller as
Secretary of the Treasury, Winthrop Rockefeller as Secretary of
Agriculture, Laurance Rockefeller as Secretary of the Interior, John . . ."

"*If that's what he is, you've got to give him credit for trying not to be too abominable.*"

"*You may get away with evading tithes for a while, but sooner or later they always catch up with you.*"

WEEKEND GUESTS

"They *said* they'd be on the six-o'clock."

"Now, we're not terribly fancy . . ."

"Well, if you don't feel like tennis, golf, croquet, or swimming, are there any of them you might like to _watch_?"

"When we started to leave, he cried."

"George!"

"Good idea! A picnic lunch at the beach from one to three. That leaves a gap of two hours between the beach and the Walkers' cocktail party."

"If they aren't down by noon, I'm going to go up and pound on the door."

"Say—uh—do you people ever like to take a quick nap after lunch?"

"Thank heaven! I've finally discovered something they like to do."

"Guess who doesn't eat seafood."

"Hey, Mary, come on out and see the sunset."

"I hope _you're_ good, Charlie. I've only played a couple of times."

"Sh-h-h! If they know we're awake, we'll have to go and <u>do</u> something."

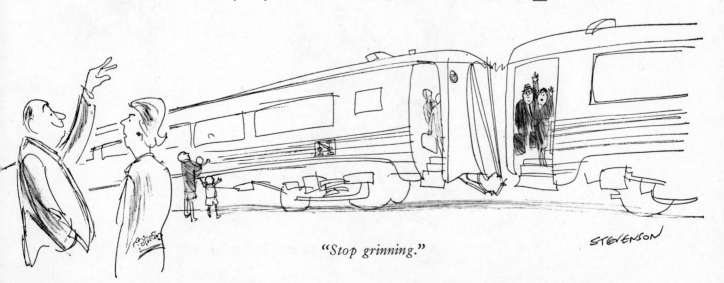

"Stop grinning."

"The committee is now in session. Have any of you gentlemen got any special bills you'd like bottled up?"

"Say, isn't that George Burckhart and his boys?"

"*Congratulations, Shaeffer! You are now the captain.*"

"But, dear, I thought you _wanted_ it shaped like a pyramid."

"Aeschylus is good, I suppose, but I go to the theatre to relax."

"*Lest we be accused of contributing to inflation later on, let's vote ourselves a good little raise right here and now.*"

"*Hey, where is everybody?*"

"I haven't decided which I prefer, Luke—full parity through supply-management controls, marketing quotas, and land retirement with conservation practices or . . ."

"The state the world's in, Polly, all I'm planting is annuals."

"*Listen, Paluzzi, as long as you're working for Scarpi Costruzioni, I don't want to hear any more of your 'Rome wasn't built in a day' stuff.*"

"I just don't like his looks—so far."

"Good morning, sir. I'm making a survey. Could you tell me which Presidential candidate you're—uh—against?"

CHERRY~BLOSSOM TIME

"Where's the F.B.I.?"

"And this, I suppose, is where all the hanky-panky goes on."

"Nobody lives in there. It's so that when people see it they'll remember George Washington."

"If you really and truly think the National Gallery of Art is a drag, Irwin, perhaps you'd better march right back to the hotel!"

"No one leaves Statuary Hall till we find Ronald Baughman."

"But suppose we _do_ get to shake hands with him. _Then_ what do we say?"

CLOSED TO VISITORS

"It's a real comfort, honey, to know that Barry Goldwater's watching out for us in there."

"We'll settle for him or her or Caroline or the baby."

"It doesn't look like any New Frontier to me."

"What if right this minute somebody came over and told us they needed two more guys for Touch?"

"We're from New Hampshire, and we're looking for Senator Bridges' office."

"I think I'll run for the Student Council."

"It seems like every day
I get more and more grizzly."

"Do I mean something to you,
Arlene, or could this be
just anybody down here?"

"*This would seem to indicate that while they will fly three or four thousand miles over open water without resting, they have no instinctual objection to resting if a resting place were to be found.*"

"*And the irritating thing is that they'll lose themselves without a trace on Fifth Avenue.*"

"*There isn't a soul here I'd care to know socially.*"

"*According to this, we should be approaching the dry crater called the Mare Imbrium.*"

"It turns out, Estelle, that I'm not being kicked upstairs, after all. I'm being kicked downstairs."

"Well, the voice of the turtle was sure as hell heard in Fairfield County today."

"Now, get this straight, Fogarty. As long as I'm chairman of the board . . ."

"Let me put it this way, Saunders. We feel you might be happier climbing some other pyramid."

LAUNCHING
OF THE
NUCLEAR
SUBMARINE
U.S.S.
...TON

STEVENSON

*"Are you sure
it won't do something?"*

CONSTRUCTION

"It'll be made of cardboard, like the rest of them."

"*Last fall, it took me over an hour to plant one dinky lilac.*"

"*Somebody ought to be ashamed of himself.*"

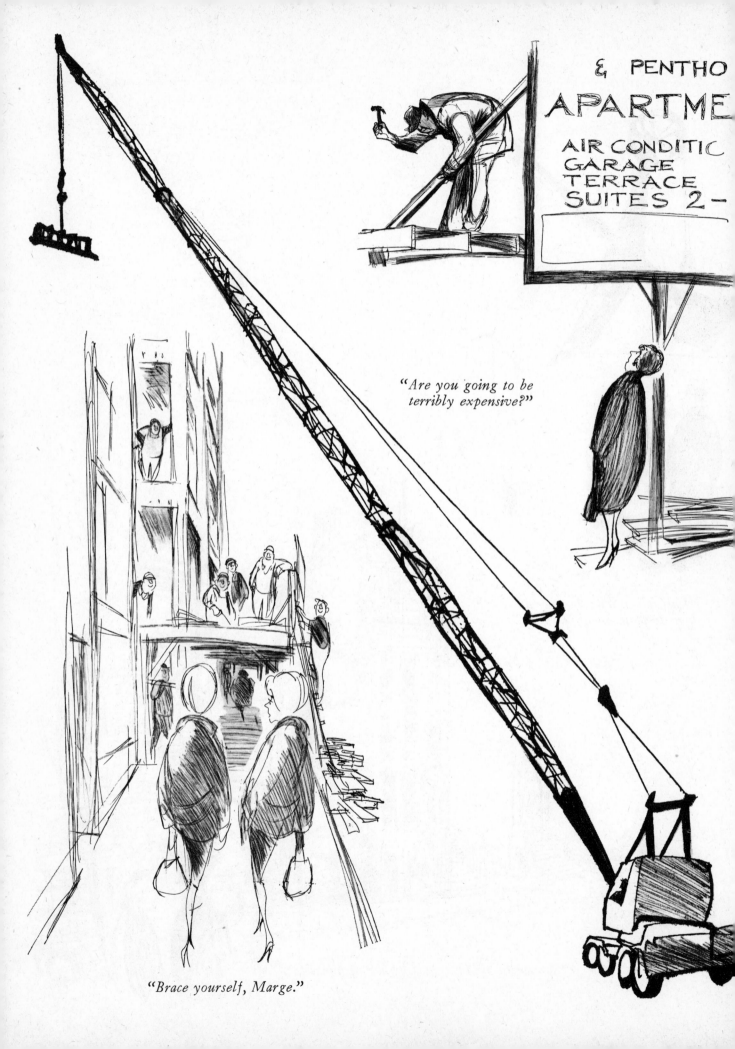

& PENTHO
APARTME
AIR CONDITIC
GARAGE
TERRACE
SUITES 2—

*"Are you going to be
terribly expensive?"*

"Brace yourself, Marge."

"*You know what I wish, Charlie? I wish they'd just fill it in and plant grass.*"

"Probably a tax gimmick."

"Damn the Uris brothers, damn the Tishmans, damn Zeckendorf . . ."

"They expect so much and we have so little to give!"

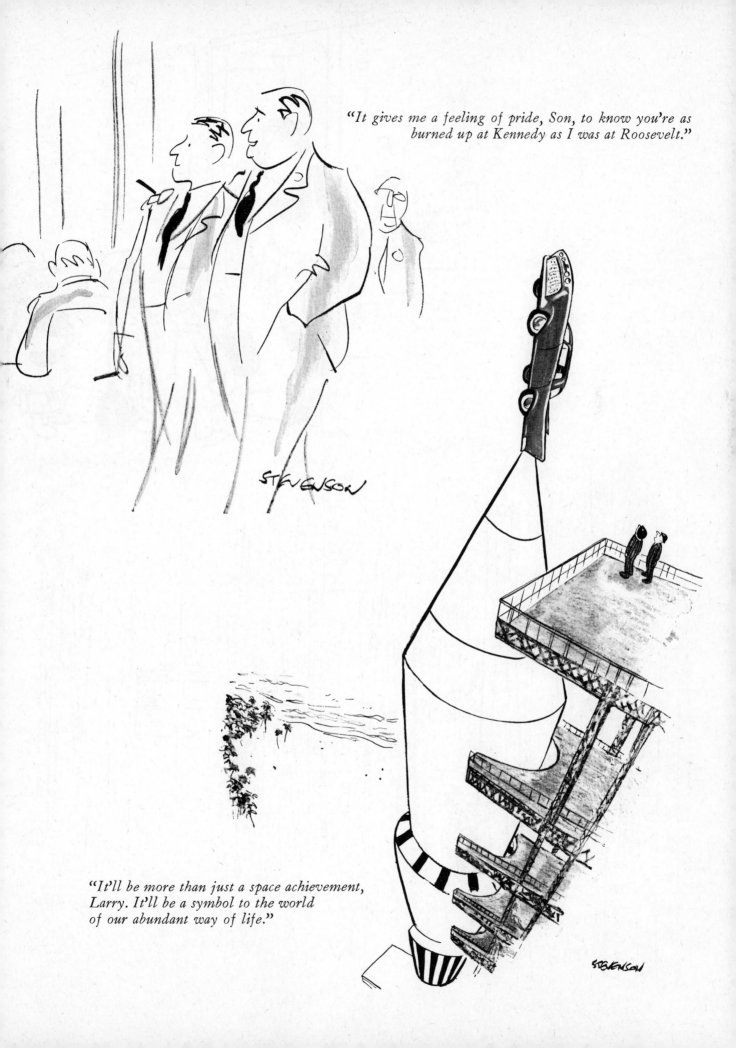

"It gives me a feeling of pride, Son, to know you're as burned up at Kennedy as I was at Roosevelt."

"It'll be more than just a space achievement, Larry. It'll be a symbol to the world of our abundant way of life."

"No, no, children! Private homes, only private homes!"

"Fellows, look! We're saved!"

"I don't feel Marie is the right sort for the Garden Club."

"Have you noticed an easing of tensions ever since the State of the Union Message?"

"I think we should keep going."

"*Listen, Townsend, when are you going to start pulling your own weight and stop this damn '*And now let's see how Tony Trevor is doing over at the other end of the Convention Hall'*?*"

"He's sure steering clear of any egghead-image overtones this year."

"You see, if you don't happen to find anything at all amusing about
him in the first place—as I don't—then, you see, you don't find it
amusing to hear this chap imitating him, don't you see."

GARDEN CENTER

"He doesn't seem very ecstatic about May."

"He always pretends he doesn't remember me."

"What have you got?"

"I see the one I want!"

"I don't care if it is a weed.
I like it."

"Now, don't sell me anything Rachel Carson wouldn't bu

"Do you have to spray it or feed it or prune it or anything?"

"Are you by any chance the Mrs. Cromwell who always won everything at Grand Central Palace?"

"It looks peaked."

"The congestion this Fourth seems worse than ever."

"When you come right down to it, I guess whatever makes him collect two pails of sea shells
in ten minutes is the same thing that made him president of Amalco at thirty-six."

"Looks like it's going to be a nice day."

"You force me to say this, Himsley. If you were really wanted on this board,
do you think your chair would still be in the carpenter shop?"

"Hey, Al, take it easy."

"We're mighty proud of our little town."

"*I've often wondered how they dealt with that problem.*"

"*Paris was sublime, and we loved the château country, and everywhere we went the French adored Horace.*"

*"Someone must love someone
very much indeed."*

"If you two don't quit arguing with each other, I'm gonna throw you both right out of here!"

"Have a nice day, dear, and try not to get toppled."

"O.K. So when we have a party, we won't ask _them_."

"I hope I'll be able to recognize the fine line between relaxing from the tensions of business and going to pot."

"It's been done."

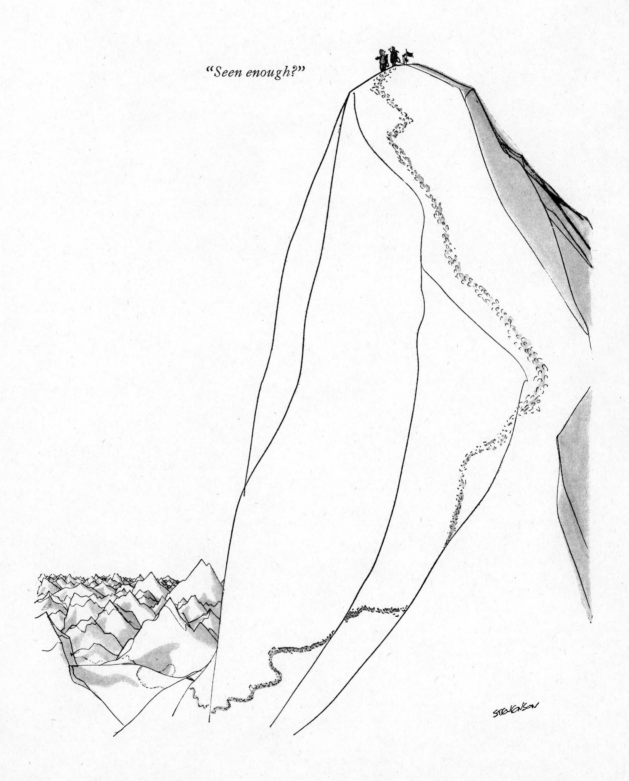

"*Seen enough?*"